More brilliant SAT Busters for KS2 Maths and English...

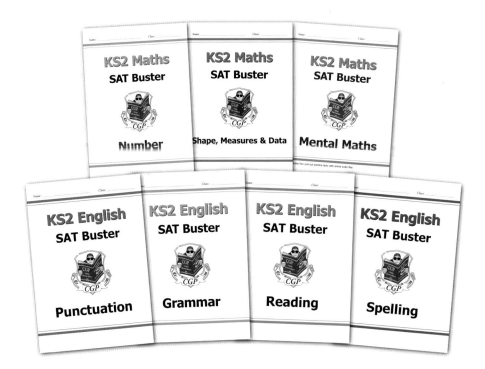

...have you got yours?

See them all at www.cgpbooks.co.uk
— or ask your teacher for more info!

No chickens were harmed in the making of this book

ISBN 978 1 84762 907 4

9 781847 629074

E6G21   £3.95
               (Retail Price)

It's another Quality Book from CGP

This book has been carefully written for Key Stage Two children learning grammar. It's full of tricky grammar exercises designed to give lots of practice for the Year 6 SATs.

Children can use the Grammagator tick boxes for self-assessment, which helps you work out how they're getting on.

What CGP is all about

Our sole aim here at CGP is to produce the highest quality books — carefully written, immaculately presented and dangerously close to being funny.

Then we work our socks off to get them out to you — at the cheapest possible prices.

Grammar Hints and Tips

Grammar can be a bit tricky, so get a firm grip on the basics and you'll be off to a good start. Here are some hints and tips for the most important bits of grammar.

1. **Learn** the **main parts** of speech.

   The <u>acrobat</u> <u>balanced</u> on the <u>wobbly</u> tightrope.

   Noun   **Verb**   **Adjective**
   (a naming word)   (a doing or   (a describing word)
                     being word)

2. Make sure you can **identify** the different **parts** of a **sentence**.

   <u>When they saw the acrobat,</u> <u>the children cheered loudly.</u>

   Subordinate Clause   **Main Clause**
   (the less important clause)   (the most important clause)

3. Make sure that the **verb agrees** with whoever is doing the action.

   The <u>child cheers</u> for the acrobat.   The <u>children cheer</u> for the acrobat.

   There is **only one** child so the   There's **more than one** child so
   verb needs to be **singular**.   the verb needs to be **plural**.

4. Check that **verbs** are written correctly in each **tense**.

   I <u>have seen</u> her.   I <u>saw</u> her.

   Not I <u>have saw</u> her.   **Not** I <u>seen</u> her.

5. Know how to spot **Non-Standard English**, like double negatives.

   I have <u>not</u> seen <u>no</u> acrobat.   I have not seen an acrobat.

   This is a **double negative**.   This is **Standard English**.

Contents

Published by CGP

Editors
Heather Gregson, Anthony Muller, Sabrina Robinson, Megan Tyler
With thanks to Claire Boulter and Janet Berkeley for the proofreading.

ISBN: 978 1 84762 907 4

www.cgpbooks.co.uk
Clipart from Corel®
Printed by Elanders Ltd, Newcastle upon Tyne.
Based on the classic CGP style created by Richard Parsons.

Text, design, layout and original illustrations © Coordination Group Publications Ltd. (CGP) 2012
All rights reserved.

Photocopying this book is not permitted. Extra copies are available from CGP with next day delivery.
0870 750 1242 • www.cgpbooks.co.uk

Section 1 — Types of Word

Nouns

Nouns are naming words. They're really important — if we didn't have names for things, life would be chaos. Have a go at the questions and you'll be an expert in no time.

1. Circle the noun in each of the phrases below.

   a. the talking robot   c. eating a sandwich   e. snowman slowly melting

   b. a sticky bun   d. balloons bursting loudly   f. next to the jelly

2. Circle all the nouns below.

   tiny   slime   potato   hair   brilliant   discover

   car   write   computer   ogre   quickly   after

3. Write a sentence which includes all of the following nouns.

   a. **teacher**   **coffee**   **desk**

   ....

   b. **mountain**   **cabin**   **climber**

   ....

4. Underline the two nouns in the sentence below.

   The curious kangaroo peered into their tent.

   Now write your own sentence which includes those two nouns.

   ....

You may have done a page on naming words, but have you earned the name of Grammagator? Tick the box.

Singular and Plural Nouns

1. Complete the table below with the nouns in their singular and plural form.

Singular	Plural
....	monkeys
glass	....
dragon	....
....	potatoes

2. In the boxes below, write whether each noun is singular (S) or plural (P).

tree ☐   **clouds** ☐   **bells** ☐   **goose** ☐   **gentlemen** ☐

3. Write down the plural forms of each of the nouns below.

mystery ⇒ ....   **wolf** ⇒ ....   **sheep** ⇒ ....

foot ⇒ ....   **child** ⇒ ....   **holiday** ⇒ ....

4. For each of the word pairs in brackets, cross out the option that does not make sense.

a. His (**shirt / shirts**) is dirty and his (**shoes / shoe**) are full of holes.

b. The (**guest / guests**) have arrived and the (**table / tables**) is set.

c. The (**wall / walls**) are made of gingerbread and the (**roof / roofs**) is made of sugar.

d. Sam's (**sock / socks**) are stinky but his (**trainer / trainers**) smell worse.

e. My (**cousin / cousins**) travel a lot but my (**sister / sisters**) prefers to stay at home.

Grammagators know all about singular and plural nouns. Do you? Tick the box to show how you did.

Section 1 — Types of Word

Types of Noun

1. Match up each type of noun with its definition.

Type of Noun	Definition

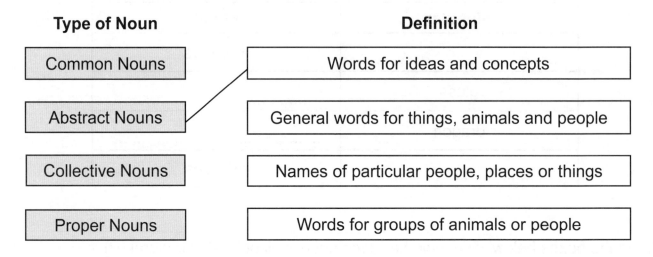

Common Nouns

Abstract Nouns

Collective Nouns

Proper Nouns

Words for ideas and concepts

General words for things, animals and people

Names of particular people, places or things

Words for groups of animals or people

2. Explain how you can always spot a proper noun, even if you don't know what it means.

    ....

3. Match each collective noun to the correct animal.

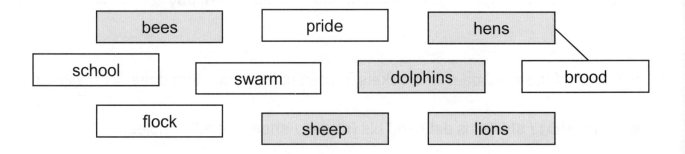

bees   pride   hens

school   swarm   dolphins   brood

flock   sheep   lions

4. Circle all the proper nouns in the sentences below.

    a. Elizabeth loves to roller-skate beside the Thames in a tutu.

    b. The old sailor told Rufus stories about his travels across the Pacific Ocean.

    c. The twins were very excited about their trip to France on Sunday.

    d. Mr Mason always went to the supermarket on a Tuesday night after work.

   © CGP 2012

Types of Noun

5. Circle the abstract nouns in the box below.

painting	sweets	love	sour
quickly	happiness	cave	boredom	wizard
jealousy	toad	frost	red	anger

(An abstract noun is something that you cannot see, hear, smell or touch.)

6. Label the nouns in the sentences below as either common, proper or collective nouns.

<u>Gertrude</u> went on safari in <u>Kenya</u> last year and saw a <u>herd</u> of African <u>elephants</u>.

<u>Max</u> turned and saw the <u>wolf</u> break away from its <u>pack</u> and race towards the <u>car</u>.

7. a. Write your own sentence which contains a common, a proper and an abstract noun.

....

....

b. Write your nouns in the correct space in the table below.

Common	Proper	Abstract

The collective noun for a Grammagator is a "syntax".
A syntax of Grammagators. Are you one of the syntax?

© CGP 2012

Pronouns

Pronouns are those handy little words that save you repeating nouns. You use them loads.

1. Circle the pronouns below.

> me   name   hat   Linda   trees
>
> Bernie's   hers   they   radio   him
>
> dancers   ours   nurse   you

2. Rewrite the sentences, replacing the underlined nouns with the correct pronoun.

    a. Den bought wine gums even though <u>Den</u> doesn't really like <u>wine gums</u>.

    ....

    ....

    b. <u>My pizza</u> was better than <u>Ishaq and Rashid's pizza</u>.

    ....

    ....

3. Cross out the incorrect pronoun in the sentences below.

    George and (**I / me**) had a cheese rolling competition.

    My uncle took my sister and (**me / I**) on a tour of his spaghetti factory.

    Freddie and (**me / I**) fell out because I pushed (**he / him**) in the duck pond.

    They awarded the prize to Ollie and (**I / me**), and both of (**we / us**) were really proud.

How do you feel about pronouns? Are you an advanced Grammagator or still a beginner? Tick the box.

    © CGP 2012

Articles

The three articles are 'a', 'an' and 'the'. They're little words but you can't forget about them.

1. Tick the version of each sentence which uses articles correctly.

   a. I play the football every Saturday. ☐   I play football every Saturday. ☐

   b. Shani painted the neighbour's cat. ☐   Shani painted neighbour's cat. ☐

   c. My sister is afraid of heights. ☐   My sister is afraid of the heights. ☐

   d. She wanted to buy xylophone. ☐   She wanted to buy the xylophone. ☐

2. Choose **a**, **an** or **the** to fill in the gaps in the sentences below.

   This is .... easy page of maths sums

   My brother is training to be .... astronaut at .... moment.

   Please bring me .... loaves of bread from .... kitchen.

   Miriam had .... headache after listening to .... loud music.

3. Rewrite the passage so that the articles are used correctly.

   In the August I went to a acrobatics display. It lasted for a hour but a best bit of an day
   was a magic show that followed a display. After an show, I had the cupcake at
   my favourite café on a main street.

   ....

   ....

   ....

   ....

Articles are small but mighty. Did you conquer the exercises on articles, oh young Grammagator?

Verbs

Verbs are doing words — if I were you, I'd be doing these excellent exercises on using them.

1. Circle all the verbs below.

swims	spinach	grinning	cardboard	sang	discover
vest	write	megaphone	has	angrily	were	nervous

2. Underline the verbs in these sentences.

Poor Ikram tripped over the cat and fell flat on her face.

They enjoyed the concert but it lasted too long.

When Jakub showed me his pet tarantula, I fainted.

Liliana likes gravy on her chips but I prefer curry sauce.

3. Cross out the incorrect form of the verb in the sentences below.

Matilda (**tells / tell**) jokes all the time.   I never (**do / does**) chores at home.

Ed and Ali (**has / have**) the same birthday.   They (**shares / share**) it with me.

Lara (**saves / save**) her crisp packets.   My sister (**eats / eat**) cold baked beans.

4. Rewrite this sentence so it is about yourself.

He likes to read horror stories even though he is scared of ghosts.

....

....

            © CGP 2012

Verbs

5. Underline the verb in each sentence and write who is doing the action.

Mr Smith <u>cooks</u> dinner every night for Mrs Smith.   *Mr Smith*

At Yanika's party, Olivia danced the most.   ....

Owen threw the boomerang to Rhys.   ....

Akash changed the light bulb for his granny.   ....

Petra's dog always licks her face.   ....

6. Join up the correct parts of the sentences so that they make sense.

Spencer	bakes great cakes	as he crossed the finish line.
Aunty Liz	missed their bus	and she always saves me some.
Claire and I	waved his arms	so we could raise some money.
Jo and Sam	sold our old stuff	so they had to walk to school.

7. Write a sentence using the verbs and people given below.

to swim   **Tamara and Chris**

....

to eat   **Priti and I**

....

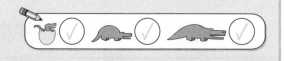

So, my friend, how did you do with your doing words?
Tick the box to show how well you did.

Verb Tenses

1. The verbs in bold are in the wrong tense. Write the correct version on the line.

   Yesterday, Greg **eats** three slugs to win a dare.   ....

   Oliver will **took** part in the dance competition.   ....

   He's absolutely sure he **knew** where he's going.   ....

   My grandad's parrot can **sang** "Happy Birthday".   ....

   I nearly **has** my hand bitten off by a llama.   ....

   You **laughed** when you see their fancy dress tonight.   ....

2. **I go to the pool and I swim ten lengths. Then I jump in from the diving board.**

   a. Rewrite these sentences in the past tense.

      ....

      ....

   b. Rewrite these sentences in the future tense.

      ....

      ....

3. Write the words in brackets in the correct tense to complete the paragraph.

   Fatima and Ayesha often (go) .... shopping. Last weekend they

   (travel) .... by train to Birmingham to go to the shopping centre.

   They (eat) .... lunch at a coffee shop and (choose) ....

   a birthday present for their dad. They (have) .... a great time and

   (agree) .... that they would definitely go again soon.

                                            © CGP 2012

Verb Tenses

4. Cross out the incorrect verbs to complete each sentence below.

   Our neighbour (**sat / sit / sits**) in the bath and sings opera every night.

   Mum (**bought / buy / brought**) ten tins of beans at the supermarket.

   My stepbrother (**passes / passed / past**) his driving test last week.

   My little sister always (**breaked / broke / breaks**) her toys when she is cross.

   Tau (**does / done / did**) his homework yesterday so he could relax today.

5. Rewrite each sentence using the correct form of the verb in brackets.

   Anitchka wondered when her lost poodle (**will / would / shall**) come home.

   ....

   ....

   Today (**should / was / must**) have been a great day, but everything went wrong.

   ....

   ....

   Amy tried to ride a camel but (**can / could / will**) not keep her balance.

   ....

   ....

6. Write your own sentence in the future tense beginning: **"Next Sunday, I will..."**

   ....

   ....

Verb Tenses

7. Rewrite each sentence, changing it into the tense in brackets.

    He went to Mexico to buy a polka dot poncho.   (Future tense)

    ....

    We look after our aunty's pet ostrich.   (Past tense)

    ....

    I will get lots of chocolate on my birthday.   (Present tense)

    ....

8. Write the correct version of each verb on the line.

    Dear Sir or Madam,

          I am **write** to complain about a bag of crisps that I **buy** last weekend.
    ⬆   ⬆

    ....

    In the packet I **find** a snail. I was so shocked that I **scream** and **drop** the packet.
    ⬆   ⬆   ⬆

    ....

    I will never **ate** your crisps again and I hope you will **gave** me a refund.
    ⬆   ⬆

    ....

          Yours faithfully,

          Tom Wilkins

Grammagators know all about verb tenses. Do you?
Tick the box to show how you did.

Active and Passive Verbs

1. Write whether each sentence is active (A) or passive (P).

   a. The eggs were thrown by Marie. ☐

   b. A protest was held by the villagers. ☐

   c. The mice scared the elephants. ☐

   d. Francine knitted herself a woolly hat. ☐

   e. The old castle is haunted by ghosts. ☐

2. Read this sentence: **The superheroes saved the city from the raging fire**.

   a. Who is doing the action? ....

   b. Complete the passive form of this sentence.

   The city .... **from the raging fire by the superheroes.**

3. Rewrite these sentences as passive sentences.

   My sister spilt the custard.

   ....

   The zoo keeper released the tiger.

   ....

   The astronauts discovered a new planet.

   ....

You can't be passive if you want to do well in your SATs.
Rate yourself highly if you're an active Grammagator.

Adjectives

Adjectives describe nouns. They're great for making your writing more interesting.

1.   Circle the adjectives below.

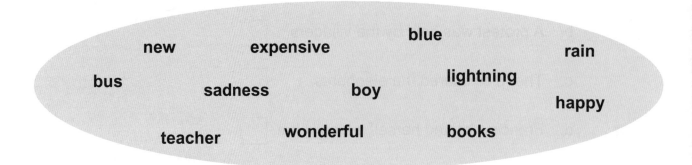

new   expensive   blue   rain

bus   sadness   boy   lightning   happy

teacher   wonderful   books

2.   Circle the adjectives in the paragraph below. There are seven in total.

> **My nan can make the most delicious cookies. They are always soft and chewy in the middle and crumbly at the edges. I love to eat them when they are hot from the oven so that the chocolate is still warm and gooey.**

3.   Underline the correct adjective to complete each sentence.

My drawing of a fish is (**better / gooder / best**) than yours.

The weather on the school trip was the (**worst / worse / baddest**) we've ever had.

I think Tariq has (**much / most / more**) computer games than I do.

4.   Join the nouns below with the most appropriate adjective.

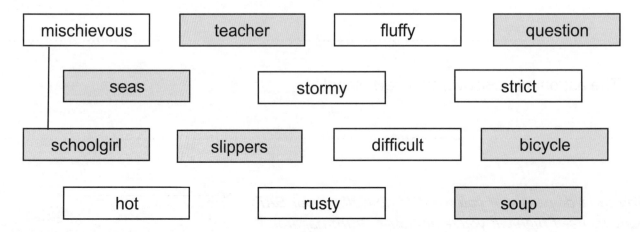

mischievous	teacher	fluffy	question
seas	stormy	strict
schoolgirl	slippers	difficult	bicycle
hot	rusty	soup

© CGP 2012

Adjectives

5. Fill in the blanks with adjectives from the box below.

One day Peter decided to hide in his .... toy shop before closing time,

so he could spend the night there. When the owner left, he was very ....

that his plan had worked. First he played for hours with the .... games

consoles. Then he built a .... race course for the remote control

cars. Finally, he raced around on the .... bikes until he was exhausted,

and then fell asleep on the .... toys. The next morning the shop owner

was .... Peter had made a .... mess.

excited	latest	favourite	furious
complicated	cuddly	fastest	terrible

6. Replace the underlined adjectives with a more interesting adjective.

It was a <u>nice</u> day so I thought it would be <u>nice</u> to go fishing at the <u>nice</u> lake.

The party was <u>bad</u>. The food was <u>bad</u> and the music was <u>bad</u>. I had a <u>bad</u> time.

7. Write a sentence using these three adjectives: **hot, yellow, careful**

....

....

Grammagators like to be described as grammartastic.
Are you a fantastic, grammartastic Grammagator?

Adverbs

Adverbs describe doing words. Here's an example. I bet you'll do these exercises <u>brilliantly</u>.

1. Underline the adverbs in the sentences below.

    a.   Along the coast the mist rolled in spookily.

    b.   Talib flipped the pancakes expertly.

    c.   Becky practised often and became a famous juggler.

    d.   Xavi ran into the door because he was going so fast.

2. Sort the words below into adverbs and adjectives.

| truthful | secretly | slowly | ~~spooky~~ | open |
| tricky | carefully | ~~mysteriously~~ | baggy | quickly |

Adverbs
mysteriously
....
....
....
....

Adjectives
....
....
....
....
....

3. Cross out the adverb that doesn't fit in with the rest of the sentence.

    The wind blows more (**bitterly / cleverly**) in winter.

    My stomach grumbles (**loudly / loosely**) when I am hungry.

    The cockroach scuttled (**hurriedly / warmly**) over my feet.

© CGP 2012

Adverbs

4. For each sentence, write in the best adverb from the options. Use each adverb once.

.... my friends and I have arguments.

I .... forget to feed my pet goldfish.

.... I will get that new DVD for my birthday.

I hoped that the guests would arrive ....

soon

perhaps

never

sometimes

5. Sort the adverbs in the box below to match the phrases they best describe.

hard   snugly   brightly   ~~dimly~~   perfectly
    busily   faintly   quietly   tightly

coals glowing...	people working...	gloves fitting...
dimly	....	....
....	....	....
....	....	....

6. Choose an appropriate adverb to go in the space in each of these sentences.

The elephants splashed .... in the water hole.

The students ran .... out of the school gates.

The crocodile moved .... through the river.

The magician's assistant vanished ....

Grammagators sit their SATs confidently. After these
pages, how confident a Grammagator are you?

Prepositions

Prepositions tell you how things are related in a sentence. The exercises on this page should help you get to grips with them. Have a go and see for yourself...

1. Circle the prepositions below.

under	buried	orange	rising
real	into	on top of	cloud
lay	flying	over	after

2. Choose a suitable preposition to complete each sentence.

around   from   between   out of   over
at   under   to   in

My cousin is a pilot and travels all .... the world.

The burglar made his escape by jumping .... the window.

The climber wrapped her scarf .... her head.

The clown stood .... the bridge.

3. Underline the preposition in each sentence and write down whether it shows time or place.

a. The alarm went off <u>during</u> the assembly.   ....*time*............................

b. Beverly lives opposite the sweet shop.   ....

c. Marcus was exhausted after the match.   ....

d. My dad snored throughout the film.   ....

e. They tied ribbons around the gifts.   ....

    © CGP 2012

Prepositions

4. For each sentence below, write whether the word in bold is an adverb or a preposition.

The waiter told him to stand **up**.   *adverb*
....

We left the mouldy cheese **in** the car.   ....

The champion runner finished miles **ahead**.   ....

The purple monkey is **next to** the dishwasher.   ....

They were really full **after** the buffet.   ....

The rain came pouring **down**.   ....

5. Write a preposition that makes sense in each of the blank spaces below.

> To find the ancient treasure you need to go a hundred miles ....
>
> the desert. Go east .... the oasis and then travel ....
>
> the sand dunes until you come to a pyramid. .... the pyramid is a
>
> statue of a sphinx. The treasure is buried .... it.

6. Write a sentence using each set of words below, including your own preposition.
    When you have finished each sentence, write your preposition on the dotted line.

jumped   **shocked**   ....

....

fridge   **disgusting**   ....

....

Where do you stand on prepositions, Grammagator?
Are you on top of them? Tick the box.

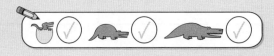

Mixed Practice

You've reached the end of Section One. Now it's time to see how great you are at grammar. These exercises will test all of the topics covered so far. Go get 'em...

1. Match the type of word to the correct definition.

A word that names something or someone.	Noun
A word that describes how an action is done.	Adjective
A word that tells you what someone or something is doing.	Adverb
A word that tells you how things are related.	Preposition
A word that saves you from repeating a noun.	Pronoun
A word that describes a noun.	Verb

2. Sort the words below into the correct columns.

~~sweetly~~	delicate	teapot	grumpily
learn	arrived	shiny	gardener
laughter	nervously	apple	cried
nervous	briskly	suggested	lazy

Noun	Verb	Adverb	Adjective
....	....	*sweetly*	....
....	....	....	....
....	....	....	....
....	....	....	....

© CGP 2012

Mixed Practice

3. Match each label below to the correct word in the sentence.

(Laurie) ran quickly towards the ball.

Verb	Proper noun	Common noun	Adverb

The students whispered nervously when they saw the headmaster.

Pronoun	Adverb	Singular noun	Plural noun

The herd of hungry cows plodded across the field.

Collective noun	Verb	Preposition	Adjective

Katrin and June went over the road to meet their new neighbours.

Preposition	Article	Adjective	Plural noun

4. Cross out the incorrect options in the sentences below.

Valentina keeps (**her / she**) money (**into / in**) the freezer.

I waited for (**an / a**) hour but in the end (**they / them**) did not arrive.

Brutus wished that he (**had / have**) not (**ate / eaten**) the entire cake.

We took (**the / an**) new kayak out (**on / in**) the lake as it was a nice day.

Omar and (**I / me**) had to run to the shop before (**it / they**) closed.

They gave Lizzie and (**I / me**) (**a / an**) pair of socks for us to share.

Mixed Practice

5. Label the underlined words with the correct word type. Be as specific as you can.

Jasvinder had never *travelled* abroad before because she had *a* terrible *fear* of flying.

proper noun			

The picnic came to a sudden end when a gaggle of angry geese charged at us.

Liz waited patiently, hiding under the bed until she was sure the coast was clear.

6. a. Complete each sentence, making sure you use an **adverb**. Circle the adverbs.

We heard a strange noise ....

Miguel liked to ....

b. Complete each sentence, making sure you use an **adjective**. Circle the adjectives.

On his way to school Jamie noticed ....

In my family ....

c. Complete each sentence. Make sure each one is written as a **passive** sentence.

The clues were found ....

His homework was ....

     © CGP 2012

Mixed Practice

7. Underline the error in each sentence and write the correction in the space provided.

I am <u>go</u> to my salsa lesson, but I'll be back soon. ....*going*..............

They gave him free muffins so him would return. ....

Eating cheese before bed can gives you bad dreams. ....

Clownfish is the comedians of the ocean. ....

8. Read this paragraph and answer the questions below.

New evidence for life on other planets was revealed by scientists today. A group of specialists have been eagerly studying the creatures to find out more about them. The leader of the investigation, Dr Specs, claims that he has seen small, green creatures crawling across the surface of a nearby planet. Many excited people have gathered outside his laboratory throughout the day.

a. Underline the passive sentence.

b. Write down an adverb which is used in this paragraph.

   ....

c. Which two adjectives are used to describe the creatures?

   ....

d. Which adjective describes the people who have gone to the laboratory?

   ....

e. Circle the prepositions in the text.

Wow, that was a whole lot of practice! After that, do you feel like the leader of the Grammagators?

Section 2 — Writing Sentences

Sentences

Sentences need to make sense. See if you can turn these sentences into sense-tences.

1. Tick or cross to show whether each sentence makes sense or not.

    a. When we went into the cave saw treasure. ☐

    b. If you like the leotard, you should wear it. ☐

    c. Look outside, you can see a flying saucer! ☐

    d. If I come to visit your family. ☐

2. Write down whether each sentence is a statement, question or command.

    a. How many camels can you fit in a caravan ....

    b. I have lots of ideas for birthday presents ....

    c. Is there enough time to wash the cat ....

    d. Please take out the rubbish ....

3. Using all of the words below, fill in the gaps in this text so that it makes sense.

minutes	stir	put	bowl	mixture	gone

Sift 120 g of plain flour into a .... Break 2 eggs into the mixture and

.... well. Slowly add the milk and carry on stirring until all the milk has

.... some butter in a frying pan and heat it until it

melts. Then, pour in the pancake .... until the bottom of the frying pan is

covered. Cook the pancake for about two .... until it's golden in colour.

You are accused of being a Grammagator. It's time for your sentencing and to tick how well you've done.

© CGP 2012

Paragraphs

Paragraphs are groups of sentences and here's a group of questions about them.

1. Tick all of the boxes that correctly describe when you should start a new paragraph.

    After every four sentences ☐

    When you are talking about a different place ☐

    When you are writing what someone thinks ☐

    When a new person speaks ☐

    When you are talking about a different time ☐

    After a long conversation ☐

2. Read each sentence below and in the box, write a 'T' if it is true or an 'F' if it is false.

    Paragraphs contain sentences that talk about the same thing. ☐

    A new paragraph doesn't start on a new line. ☐

    Paragraphs are made up of sentences that follow on from each other. ☐

    Paragraphs make a piece of writing easier to read. ☐

3. Read this piece of text and mark where new paragraphs should begin with //.

    There was a loud crash inside the warehouse as the two burglars clumsily fell in through the window. "Be quiet!" the larger burglar, Larry, told his companion. "Sorry," replied John, a skinny man, as he dusted himself off. Meanwhile, across the road, little Harry Spratt woke up in bed, wondering what all the racket was. He peered out of the window and saw the light of two torches moving inside the warehouse. He wanted to investigate but he knew better than to put himself in danger. Instead, Harry called the police. Fifteen minutes later, he stood at his front door and watched as the police arrested the two burglars and marched them outside. "Good work, young man," the police sergeant said, patting him on the head.

Clever Grammagators know how to make their writing clear. Do you? Tick the box to show how you did.

Phrases

A phrase is a small group of words which forms part of a sentence. Have a go at these...

1. Join up each phrase with the correct type.

Very slowly		Noun Phrase
Blue leather shoes		Prepositional Phrase
Under the stairs		Adverb Phrase

If you're not sure what kind of phrase it is, look at the main word types in each phrase.

2. Underline the noun phrase in each of these sentences. Then rewrite the sentence, replacing the noun phrase with the correct pronoun.

The neighbour's dog barked loudly. ....*It barked loudly.*..............................

Who owns the pink unicycle? ....

We don't like horror films. ....

I ate an entire roast chicken. ....

I have met many famous pop stars. ....

3. Circle all the adverb phrases in the box below.

she has spoken	very bravely	favourite book
	new games	extremely clearly
too loudly		even though
surprisingly well	dangerously fast	annoying sister

Phrases

4. Write two sentences which include the adverb phrase **'as quickly as possible'**.

1) ....

2) ....

A preposition tells you where or when something is in relation to other things.

5. Write out the prepositional phrase for each sentence.

a. Jill jumped out of the plane. ....*out of the plane*...............

b. He walked along the tightrope slowly. ....

c. The sausages are next to the rolls. ....

d. The rabbit hopped straight towards us. ....

e. Before lunch, I wash my hands. ....

6. Write down whether each phrase is an adverb phrase (A) or a noun phrase (N).

a. fifty pounds ☐   g. angry bees ☐

b. terribly slowly ☐   h. extremely brightly ☐

c. summer weather ☐   i. my friend's chair ☐

d. these teachers ☐   j. this colour ☐

e. so happily ☐   k. her best jam ☐

f. more cheerfully ☐   l. far too early ☐

Grammagators find phrases easy — in fact, they eat them for breakfast. How well do you know phrases?

Section 2 — Writing Sentences

Clauses

If you liked phrases, then you're going to love clauses. They're like long lost cousins.

1. Put a tick in the correct column to show whether each group of words is a phrase, a main clause or a subordinate clause.

If you can't decide between a phrase and a subordinate clause, remember that subordinate clauses usually have a verb and someone doing the action.

	Phrase	Main Clause	Subordinate Clause
he fell over			
out of pocket			
before we went out			
Saturdays are the best			
they jumped for joy			
when we saw him			

2. Write down whether each sentence is a compound sentence or a complex sentence.

a. We went to the park because I wanted to play football. ....*complex*........

b. They wanted some more but there was none left. ....

c. They will make a film after the TV series ends. ....

d. I might visit the zoo or I could go to the museum. ....

e. You can sing along if you want. ....

f. They built sandcastles and they swam in the sea. ....

g. The music ended while they were dancing. ....

© CGP 2012

Clauses

3. Underline the subordinate clause in each of these complex sentences.

<u>When they had found her shoes</u>, they went out of the house.

They drank a lot of water after they had played out in the sun.

If I win the mud-throwing tournament, we can have a party.

We left the room before he could start his boring story.

I fed the pig, while Lucy took the chickens for a walk.

We had to leave the zoo because a hippo had escaped.

4. Write a main clause for each of these sentences and add a comma if necessary.

When he got home...

.... even though it was cold.

Before we could say anything...

.... because he'd lost his coat.

.... while she had a shower.

5. a. Underline the relative clause in each of these sentences.

My brother was late for tea which surprised me.

Yesterday I met the man who owns the bike shop.

b. Write a relative clause for each of these sentences.

I didn't see the banana skin...

After tea I will ring the woman...

Real Grammagators have long, sharp claws that tear up clause questions. How sharp are you at clauses?

Section 2 — Writing Sentences

Conjunctions

Conjunctions are words that join parts of a sentence together. Now join me in doing these.

1. Underline the conjunction in each of these sentences.

   The volcano was spitting ash and oozing lava.

   I hated my new hair style so I shaved it all off.

   The dragon was very full after it had eaten all the marshmallows.

   They came to the party although they weren't invited.

2. Join each pair of sentences using **and**, **but** or **so**.

   We were going to go to the playground. It was raining.

   We were going to go to the playground but it was raining.

   Jiten played tennis. He played cricket.

   ....

   I am the oldest. I get to sit in the front.

   ....

   He went to buy turnips. They were sold out.

   ....

   I was starving. I ate his sandwich.

   ....

3. Write two different complex sentences which include the conjunction **because**.

   1) ....

   2) ....

                    © CGP 2012

Conjunctions

4. Join the beginning and end of each sentence using the correct conjunction.

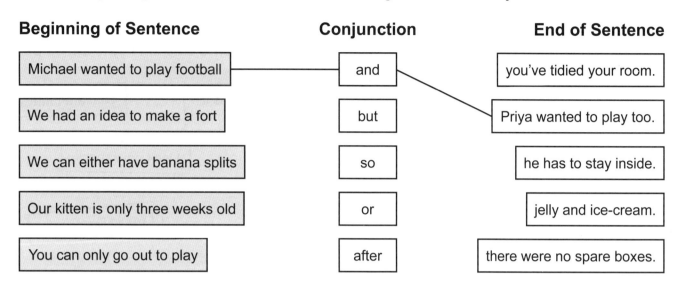

Beginning of Sentence | **Conjunction** | **End of Sentence**

Michael wanted to play football — and — Priya wanted to play too.

We had an idea to make a fort | but | you've tidied your room.

We can either have banana splits | so | he has to stay inside.

Our kitten is only three weeks old | or | jelly and ice-cream.

You can only go out to play | after | there were no spare boxes.

5. Choose the correct conjunction to complete these sentences. You can only use each conjunction once.

before   ~~while~~   unless   although

until   since   when

..........*While*.......... you were in the bathroom, I did my hair.

Let's stop him .... his jokes get any worse.

.... she gets a pony for her birthday, she will be angry.

.... I like tomato sauce, I hate tomatoes.

I'm not talking to you .... you've given me back my lizard.

.... my dad dances, I go red with embarrassment.

.... he went into space, he hasn't talked about anything else.

So how did you do? Are you a Grammagator <u>or</u> are you a Grammar-hater? <u>And</u> the answer is...

Standard vs. Non-Standard

It pays to write in Standard English. Mmm... lots of lovely marks —
much better than money. See if you can set a high standard for yourself.

1. Sort these phrases into Standard English and Non-Standard English in the tables below.

It's all mine.

This is delicious.

Who wants it?

That are funny.

He's the butcher's son.

They has no idea.

I isn't going back.

He were well good.

He can run real quick.

I would like to stay.

Standard English
....
....
....
....
....

Non-Standard English
....
....
....
....

2. Match up each sentence on the left with the correct Standard English form.

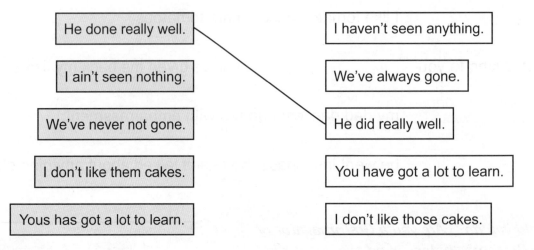

He done really well.

I ain't seen nothing.

We've never not gone.

I don't like them cakes.

Yous has got a lot to learn.

I haven't seen anything.

We've always gone.

He did really well.

You have got a lot to learn.

I don't like those cakes.

© CGP 2012

Standard vs. Non-Standard

3. Give the Standard English version of each of these sentences.

I have fell over yesterday. ....

How many moneys do you have? ....

Here's the book what I bought. ....

4. Cross out the incorrect option so that each sentence is in Standard English.

(**I done / I did**) a drawing of all of my friends.

(**They goes / They go**) to the supermarket.

(**That was / That were**) really clever of you.

(**I been / I have been**) there loads of times before.

Somebody (**has given / has gave**) us a present.

I don't know if (**they am / they are**) going to win the race.

5. Write out each sentence below in Standard English.

I never did nothing. ....

They shouldn't of been here. ....

You didn't go nowhere. ....

We couldn't of seen anything. ....

There's not nobody who knows. ....

Time to decide how well you did. Did you set a high standard, or are standards slipping? You tell me...

© CGP 2012

Section 2 — Writing Sentences

Mixed Practice

I just can't get enough of questions. Luckily there are four more pages of mixed practice questions to test everything you've learnt in this section.

© CGP 2012

1. a. Use the correct punctuation to end each of these sentences correctly.
    Then, write whether each sentence is a statement, question or command.

    (The underlined words are for part 1b.)

    Where have you been <u>all afternoon</u> ?. ....*question*..............

    <u>When the dog barked,</u> everyone looked up ....

    Does this mean that <u>your guitar is broken</u> ....

    Stop doing cartwheels <u>while I'm speaking</u> ....

    They spent <u>all morning indoors</u> watching TV ....

    <u>You looked scary</u> in your vampire costume ....

    b. Put each underlined group of words in the sentences above in the correct table.

Phrase	Main Clause	Subordinate Clause
all afternoon	....	....
....	....	....

2. Using only conjunctions, fill in the gaps in this text so that it makes sense.

    "Have you seen Karen .... Rajesh this morning?" Mrs Tomkins

    asked. "They were supposed to be having a piano lesson ....

    nobody's seen them." Eventually Mrs Tomkins left the room. ....

    she had gone, Rajesh and Karen came out from under their desks. They didn't

    want to go to their lesson .... they hadn't practised all week.

  © CGP 2012

Mixed Practice

3   a. Write each of these commands as a question.

Make my dinner!   ....

Go to your room!   ....

Bring me the remote!   ....

Clean up the kitchen!   ....

b. Write each of these statements as a question.

Alex is tired.   ....

They are early.   ....

You are busy.   ....

We are happy.   ....

4. Finish these questions so that they make sense.

Why ....

Is there ....

Have you ....

5. Write a short passage which includes all of the conjunctions below.
You can only use each conjunction once.

because	but	and	although	when

....

....

....

Mixed Practice

6. Write out the sentences below in Standard English.

    We has been well busy.   ....

    How much people are here?   ....

    You run more quicker than me.   ....

    It isn't no joke.   ....

    I slept really good last night.   ....

    We seen loads of stuff.   ....

    She was teached differently.   ....

7. Circle all of the conjunctions below.

    | even though | because | when | before | outside |

    | my | for | again | underneath |

    | who | soon | unless | never mind | but |

8. Tick or cross to show whether the relative clause is underlined correctly.

    a. He owns the hotel which is closing down.   ☐

    b. That's the teacher who cycles to school.   ☐

    c. She wore a mask which was terrifying.   ☐

    d. I don't like the lamp that is in the living room.   ☐

Mixed Practice

9. Using all of the words below, fill in the gaps in this text so that it makes sense.

door	hungry	bowl	watched
screamed	furry	outside	cereal	mouse

As Kaye poured her .... into the bowl, something small and ....

fell out. It was a ....! Kaye couldn't believe it. Her mum ....

when it jumped out of the .... and ran across the table. Kaye ....

the mouse as it escaped. Poor thing, she thought, he was probably just ....

She opened the kitchen .... and the mouse ran .... gratefully.

10. Each of these sentences has a main clause (MC) and a subordinate clause (SC).
    Underline each of the parts and label them as in the example below.

 SC   MC

After Alex won, we all celebrated at the bowling alley.

If you let me, I will dye your hair blue.

They watch rugby every weekend because they love sports.

We have to wait until Suri has woken up from her nap.

You're not getting a bigger slice because it wouldn't be fair.

While she was watching TV, I hid the remote in the cupboard.

Grammagators love mixing with other animals...
How well did you deal with all the mixed practice?

Section 3 — Making Words

Suffixes

Suffixes are letters that you add to the end of a word to change the word's meaning. Let's go.

1. Circle the suffix in each of the words below.

    soft(ly)   playful   preferable   employment

    musician   closeness   selfless   childhood

2. Complete the word in each of these sentences by adding one of the suffixes
    from the box below.

    You should use each suffix once.

ness	ly	ish	ment	ful

    Sam thought that being grounded for six weeks was a harsh punish.............

    My mum often suffers from sea sick............. when she travels on a boat.

    The vampire had to get back quick............. to avoid the sunrise.

    Unfortunately, that's about as use............. as a chocolate teapot.

    Ele is a self............. person because she only ever thinks about herself.

3. Make as many words as you can from the root words and suffixes in the table below:

Root words			Suffixes	
pain	comfort	care	less	able
accept	help	hope	ance	ful

    ....

    ....

    ....

© CGP 2012

Suffixes

4. Cross out the word with the wrong suffix in each sentence.

    She sang that song **perfectly /** ~~**perfectful.**~~

    a. That book was very **inspirationist / inspirational**.

    b. How can you **justify / justise** spending that much money on sweets?

    c. I like my **neighbourness / neighbourhood** because everyone is very friendly.

5. Some of the words in these sentences have the wrong suffix.
    Rewrite these sentences so that all of the words have the correct suffix.

    Homework isn't enjoyful, but it's foolism to avoid it.

    ....

    A lion's powerly jaws can be dangerful.

    ....

6. Add the suffix to the root word and write the new word on the line.
    Then use the new word in a sentence.

    beauty + ful ➡ ....*beautiful*.........

    .....*It was a beautiful trifle until the dog knocked it over.*.....

    lonely + ness ➡ ....

    ....

    heavy + ly ➡ ....

    ....

    amuse + ment ➡ ....

    ....

Grammagators make short work of suffix questions.
Were you a Grammagator on these pages? Pop in a tick.

Prefixes

Don't get your prefixes and suffixes mixed up — just remember that you put prefixes at the start of words. With these questions you'll be an expert in no time at all.

1. Underline the prefix in each of these words.

    <u>bi</u>cycle   unreal   overheat   mistreat

    prehistoric   dismount   interact   disobey

2. Add the root words to the prefixes to make words to
    complete these sentences.

Prefixes		Root words	
anti	tele	action	phone
sub			way
mis	re	behave	social

    Nima travelled on the .... in New York.

    My brother had an allergic .... to the nuts he was eating.

    Fran wanted to call her friend but she could not find the ....

    Nick's sister was very .... and stayed in her room all day.

    The children don't .... in class because their teacher is strict.

3. The prefixes in bold in these sentences are incorrect.
    Rewrite the words with the correct prefixes in the space provided.

    Dan gets very **sub**happy when other people **dis**understand him.
    ⬆   ⬆

    ....

    It is **dis**appropriate to wear your pyjamas in the **semi**market.
    ⬆   ⬆

    ....

                    © CGP 2012

Prefixes

4. Draw lines to match the correct prefix to the following words.

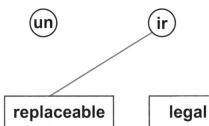

(un)	(ir)	(dis)	(il)	(in)

| replaceable | legal | healthy | secure | similar |

5. Complete the word in each of these sentences by adding one of the prefixes from the box below.

You should use each prefix once.

in	un	im	ir	dis

It is very ....likely that there will be an alien invasion.

Your explanation seems ....probable, but I'll believe you.

My dog and my cat are ....compatible — they're always fighting.

It was ....responsible to let us play with the water balloons.

Being short is a real ....advantage in basketball.

6. Add a prefix to each of the words below to create a word with the opposite meaning.

practical ....   **important** ....

clear ....   **acceptable** ....

perfect ....   **honest** ....

Grammagators prefer prefix questions to pecan pie.
How about you? It's time to tick the box...

Making Verbs

You'll be a verb-making pro before you know it if you answer all of these questions.

1. Add **-ed**, **-s** or **-ing** onto the end of these verbs to complete these sentences.

    Kate is walk.......... her ferret.

    He say.......... he has a time machine.

    Sam pass.......... his dad the salt.

    Fatima earn.......... £30 every week.

    Ali play.......... in her band last night.

    James is act.......... like an idiot.

2. Complete each sentence by adding **-ing** to the word in brackets.

    Helen is ......*travelling*...... (travel) all over the world on an alpaca.

    The stars are .... (shine) very brightly tonight.

    Ben is .... (plan) to spend all his money on novelty mugs.

    Sasha wastes so much time .... (decide) how to do her hair.

    The farmer's cows are .... (invade) our garden.

3. Add the suffix to the root word and write the new word on the line.
    Then use the new word in a sentence.

    remove + ed ➡ ....*removed*.......

    Harry removed the pens from the box and put them in his pencil case.
    ....

    believe + ed ➡ ....

    ....

    apply + ed ➡ ....

    ....

    try + ed ➡ ....

    ....

                                            © CGP 2012

Making Verbs

4. Put these verbs into the past tense by adding the suffix -**ed**.

waste ......*wasted*......   supply ....

hurry ....   bang ....

dial ....   flap ....

like ....   stay ....

5. Complete the tables below.

Verb	-ing suffix
keep	......*keeping*......
ride	....
buy	....
dig	....

Verb	-ing suffix
lie	....
win	....
fry	....
die	....

6. Write a sentence using the verb **study** with the -**s** suffix.

....

Write a sentence using the verb **stop** with the -**ed** suffix.

....

Write a sentence using the verb **have** with the -**ing** suffix.

....

Grammagators can find the right verb endings with their tails tied behind their backs. How did you do?

© CGP 2012

Mixed Practice

It's time to pull all your knowledge on suffixes and prefixes together and crack on with some mixed practice questions. These are the last questions in the book, so give them your all.

1. Sort the following words into the table according to whether they have a prefix, a suffix or both.

    ~~submerge~~   unplug   childish   reword   reality

    reconstruction   indestructible   misplaced   commitment

Prefix only	Suffix only	Prefix and Suffix
submerge		
....	....	....
....	....	....
....	....	....

2. Draw lines to match each root word to a prefix and a suffix to create a new word. Then write each new word in a sentence. Only use each box once.

Prefix	Root word	Suffix
re	polite	ly
dis	port	ance
trans	appear	ed
im	commend	ation

    The restaurant was recommended to me by a friend.
    ....

    ....

    ....

    ....

Mixed Practice

3. Complete the table below.

Word	Prefix	Root Word	Suffix
unbreakable	*un*	*break*	*able*
reworking			
disjointed			
inconsiderate			

4. All the underlined words have the wrong prefix or suffix.

Write the correct version of each word on the line.

Vikram was <u>sprinted</u> towards the theatre where he was meeting a friend.

....

He was late because he'd had a <u>lengthful</u> <u>discussing</u> with the doctor.

....

The doctor wanted to <u>autoscribe</u> him <u>transbiotics</u> for his cough.

....

5. Add a suffix to each of the nouns below to make an adjective.

fashion   *fashionable*   **like**   ....

joy   ....   **impress**   ....

accident   ....   **child**   ....

harm   ....   **friend**   ....

Mixed Practice

6. Complete these sentences by adding a suffix to the word in brackets to make a noun.

Clare was late for the ......*appointment*...... (appoint) with her fortune teller.

Elena's father always said that .... (educate) was very important.

Dan renewed his .... (member) of the swimming club.

Eva read lots of .... (inform) about pigs before buying one.

At the meeting, there was a .... (discuss) about the new park.

Luke received lots of .... (criticise) about his horrible painting.

7. Write as many words as you can by adding prefixes and suffixes to the words below.

act ....

....

pass ....

....

press ....

....

8. Write a sentence using as many words with the **in-** or **im-** prefix as you can.

....

....

Hurray — you're done! You've worked so hard that you deserve a Grammagator medal. Give yourself one last tick.

© CGP 2012

Glossary

Adjective — A word that describes a noun, e.g. **big** house, **cold** morning.

Adverb — A word that describes a verb, e.g. run **quickly**, dance **happily**.

Article — The words **the**, **a** or **an** which go before a noun.

Clause — A bit of a sentence that contains a verb and someone doing the action.

Conjunction — A word that joins two clauses or sentences, e.g. **and**, **but**, **so**.

Main clause — An important bit of a sentence that would make sense on its own,
e.g. **I went out even though it was raining.**

This bit is the main clause because 'I went out' makes sense on its own.

Noun — A word that names something, e.g. **Paul**, **scissors**, **herd**, **happiness**.

Phrase — A small part of a sentence, usually without a verb.

Prefix — Letters that can be put in front of a word to change its meaning, e.g. **un**lock.

Preposition — A word that tells you how things are related, e.g. **in**, **above**, **before**.

Pronoun — Words that can be used instead of nouns, e.g. **I**, **you**, **he**, **it**.

Subordinate clause — A less important bit of a sentence which doesn't make sense
on its own, e.g. **While you were out, I watched TV.**

This bit is the subordinate clause because 'While you were out' doesn't make sense on its own.

Suffix — Letters that can be put after a word to change its meaning, e.g. play**ful**.

Verb — A doing or being word, e.g. I **run**, he **went**, you **are**.